A·rainy·day·playbook

Our plane

Written by
Beatrice Phillpotts

Illustrated by
Margaret de Souza

AWARD PUBLICATIONS LIMITED

"It's raining, its pouring.
The old man's snoring," sang David,
dancing around the kitchen.

Emily looked out of the window.
It was raining so hard, all she could see
were raindrops chasing each other
down the glass.

"Let's go and splash in the puddles,"
cried David, grabbing his boots.

But Emily had a better idea.

"We'll build a plane," she said to David,
"and fly somewhere hot and sunny."
"Terrific!" he exclaimed, jumping up and down.

The ironing board was just the right shape for the plane's body. They hung a sheet over it to make a cabin.

"Now we need wings," said David. So he put his new surf board down across it.

"We'll need goggles," said Emily, arranging
a pair of sunglasses on Teddy's nose.
"And a parachute each," added David.

He blew up three balloons.

"This is your chief pilot speaking," said Emily loudly. "Climb aboard for a special flight to hot, sunny places."

"Hold tight, Teddy," said David
as the plane raced along the runway.
Swoosh! They were up in the air.

"Mind the birds," cried Emily as they
soared up through a flock of startled seagulls.

Soon, their house was just a tiny dot.

Teddy set a course by the sun and they
flew south.
Seas, mountains and forests
flashed by beneath them.

Then the plane started to make a funny noise.

"We've run out of petrol!" gasped Emily.
"Send out a signal for help."

At that moment
the engine stopped.

"We must make a crash landing," cried Emily.
A great desert lay below them.

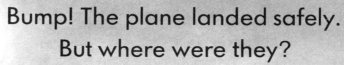

Bump! The plane landed safely.
But where were they?

"Well, it's certainly hot and sunny,"
said Emily brightly.
David and Teddy looked worried.

It got hotter.
"I'm thirsty," announced David.
"And so is Teddy."

Emily looked around her.
The sun was dazzling but she could see
a dark shape on the horizon.

"I can see some palm trees," she cried.
"Let's investigate."

But the 'trees' were moving towards them!

"They're not trees, they're people,"
said David. "They look like desert bandits."
"I hope they're friendly," he added.

The people came nearer and nearer.
"We thought you might need rescuing,"
they laughed.

It was Mum and Dad!

Better still, they had brought a big jug of
orange juice and a basket full of
sandwiches and buns with them.

So they all sat down
and had a delicious picnic
before it was time for bed.